# Practise Your Phonics With
# Julia Donaldson's
# Songbird

OXFORD
UNIVERSITY PRESS

# OXFORD

## UNIVERSITY PRESS

Great Clarendon Street, Oxford, OX2 6DP, United Kingdom

Oxford University Press is a department of the University of Oxford.
It furthers the University's objective of excellence in research, scholarship
and education by publishing worldwide. Oxford is a registered trade mark
of Oxford University Press in the UK and in certain other countries

First Edition published 2006
This Edition published 2012

British Library Cataloguing in Publication Data
Data available

978-0-19-279297-6

10 9 8 7

Printed in China

Paper used in the production of this book is a natural, recyclable product
made from wood grown in sustainable forests. The manufacturing process
conforms to the environmental regulations of the country of origin.

**Acknowledgements**
Series editor Clare Kirtley
Art edited by Hilary Wright

Help your child's learning
with essential tips, phonics
support and free eBooks
www.oxfordowl.co.uk

# Songbirds
# The Odd Pet

Story by Julia Donaldson

Pictures by Judy Brown

Series editor Clare Kirtley

OXFORD

UNIVERSITY PRESS

3

# Tips for reading The Odd Pet together

This book practises these sounds:

s m c t g p a o r l d b
f h i u v y z j n k e

Ask your child to point to these letters and say the sounds (e.g. *k* as in *kit*, not the letter name *kay*). Look out for these letters in the story.

Your child might find these words tricky:

**have now of the**

These words are common, but your child may not have learned how to sound them out yet. Say the words for your child if they do not know them.

Before you begin, ask your child to read the title by sounding out and blending as much as possible. Look at the picture together. What do you think this story is about?

Remind your child to read unfamiliar words by saying the individual sounds and then blending them together quickly to read the word. When you have finished reading the story, look through it again and:

- Ask your child, *How did Kim and Jim get a zog?* (Viv gave them one of the zogs that hatched from her zog's eggs)
- Find two words that rhyme on the first page of the story (*Kim, Jim*). Ask your child to say the middle sound in these words. Find and read some more words with the *i* sound in the middle (*Viv, sit*). Try to write some of the words. Say all of the sounds in the word separately then write the letter that makes each sound.

Kim has a cat. Jim has a dog.

But Viv has an odd pet.

It is a zog! Not a cat, not a dog, but a zog!

The zog is fat. It has ten
red legs.

It can run and hop.

It can sit and beg.

# The zog has lots of eggs!

The zog sits on the eggs.
It sits and sits.

Tap, tap, tap!
Tap, tap, tap!

# Lots of zogs!

16

# Now Kim has a cat and a zog.

# Jim has a dog and a zog.

# And Viv has ten zogs!

# Songbirds

# Miss, Miss!

Story by Julia Donaldson
Pictures by Ross Collins
Series editor Clare Kirtley

## OXFORD
UNIVERSITY PRESS

# Tips for reading Miss, Miss! together

This book practises these letter patterns:

## ll ss ff zz

Ask your child to point to these letter patterns and say the sounds (e.g. *ll* as in *full*). Look out for these letter patterns in the story.

Your child might find these words tricky:

## ball I my the

These words are common, but your child may not have learned how to sound them out yet. Say the words for your child if they do not know them.

Before you begin, ask your child to read the title by sounding out and blending. Look at the picture together. What do you think this story is about?

Remind your child to read unfamiliar words by saying the individual sounds and then blending them together quickly to read the word. When you have finished reading the story, look through it again and:

- Talk about what Miss Hill might be thinking on the last page of the story.
- Find and read words in the book which end with the sound *s* (*Miss, Tess, mess, yes, gets, bus, Ross*). Notice that the sound *s* is written in two ways (*s, ss*). Find more letter patterns on page 37 where one sound is written with two letters (*zz in buzz, ff in off, ss in Ross*).

25

# Miss Hill gets on the bus.

# Miss Hill gets off the bus.

# Songbirds

# This and That

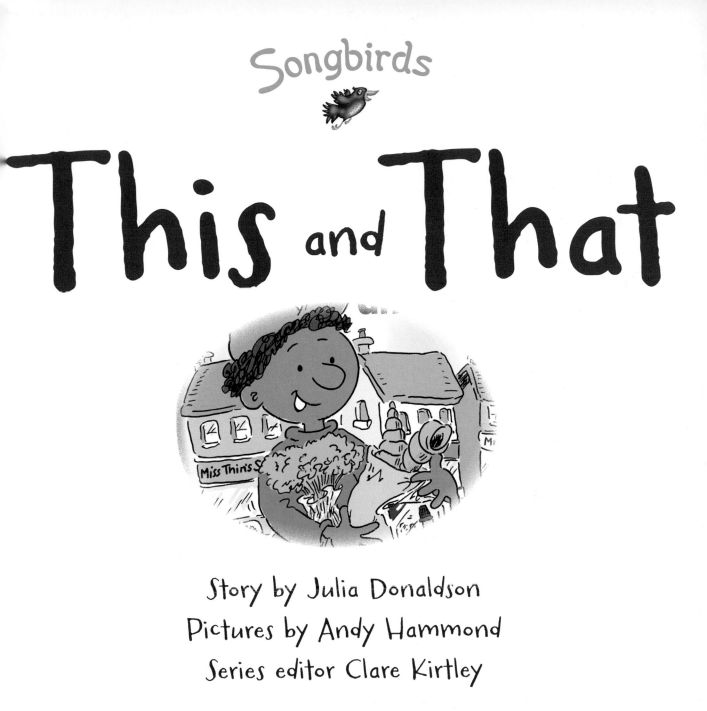

Story by Julia Donaldson
Pictures by Andy Hammond
Series editor Clare Kirtley

## OXFORD
UNIVERSITY PRESS

# Tips for reading This and That together

This book practises these letter patterns:

**sh  ch  th**

Ask your child to point to these letter patterns and say the sounds (e.g. *th* as in *thumb*). Look out for these letter patterns in the story.

Your child might find these words tricky:

**have  Mr  Mrs  some**

These words are common, but your child may not have learned how to sound them out yet. Say the words for your child if they do not know them.

Before you begin, ask your child to read the title by sounding out and blending as much as possible. Look at the picture together. What do you think this story is about?

Remind your child to read unfamiliar words by saying the individual sounds and then blending them together quickly to read the word. When you have finished reading the story, look through it again and:

- Ask your child, *How did Tim make his rabbit?*
- Find the words that begin with the *sh* sound (*shop, shell, ship*). Ask your child to point to the letter pattern which makes the beginning sound of the words (*sh*). Have fun thinking of some more words that contain the *sh* sound (*push, cash, shed, rush, dish*).

# This is Mr Chan's shop.

Mr Chan sells pens, pads and maps.

# Tim is in Mr Chan's shop.

44

# This is Miss Thin's shop.

Miss Thin sells eggs, nuts and carrots.

# Tim is in Miss Thin's shop.

49

# This is Mrs Ship's shop.

Mrs Ship sells jugs, shells and chess sets.

# Tim is in Mrs Ship's shop.

# This is Tim's rabbit!

# Songbirds

# Fish and Chips

Story by Julia Donaldson
Pictures by Jonathan Allen
Series editor Clare Kirtley

## OXFORD
UNIVERSITY PRESS

# Tips for reading Fish and Chips together

This book practises these letter patterns:

## sh  ch  th  wh

Ask your child to point to these letter patterns and say the sounds (e.g. *ch* as in *chat*). Look out for these letter patterns in the story.

Your child might find these words tricky:

## come  I'm  my  too

These words are common, but your child may not have learned how to sound them out yet. Say the words for your child if they do not know them.

Before you begin, ask your child to read the title by sounding out and blending as much as possible. Look at the picture together. What do you think this story is about?

Remind your child to read unfamiliar words by saying the individual sounds and then blending them together quickly to read the word. When you have finished reading the story, look through it again and:

- Talk about how Ron Rabbit felt at the end of the story and why (he was exhausted because the shop was very busy).
- Find words that begin or end with the *ch* sound (*chip*, *which*, *much*). Ask your child to point to the letter pattern which makes this sound (*ch*). Have fun thinking of some more words that contain the *ch* sound (*chin*, *chill*, *rich*, *such*).

This is Ron Rabbit.

Ron has a job in a fish and chip shop.

# Songbirds

# Singing Dad

Story by Julia Donaldson
Pictures by Barbara Vagnozzi
Series editor Clare Kirtley

**OXFORD**
UNIVERSITY PRESS

# Tips for reading Singing Dad together

This book practises these letter patterns:

## ng ll ff sh ch th

Ask your child to point to these letter patterns and say the sounds (e.g. *ng* as in *ring*). Look out for these letter patterns in the story.

Your child might find these words tricky:

## after all day he I'm never she singer the to

These words are common, but your child may not have learned how to sound them out yet. Say the words for your child if they do not know them.

Before you begin, ask your child to read the title by sounding out and blending. Look at the picture together. What do you think this story is about?

Remind your child to read unfamiliar words by saying the individual sounds and then blending them together quickly to read the word. When you have finished reading the story, look through it again and:

- Ask your child, *Why did Mum tell Dad off?*
- Find some words that contain the *ng* sound (*sings, long, song, fishing, digging, chopping*). Ask your child to point to the letter pattern that makes this sound (*ng*). Have fun thinking of some words that rhyme with *sing (thing, king, ring, wing)*.

# Dad is a singer.

# He sings all day long.

Song, after song,

after song, after song!

He sings to the cat and
he sings to the dog.

80

He sings in the sun

and he sings in the fog.

# He sings in the shops

and he sings in the shed.

# He sings in the bus

and he sings in his bed.

# He sings when he's fishing.

He sings when he jogs.

# He sings when he's digging

and chopping up logs.

Mum tells Dad off.
"I'm fed up with that song."

# Mum *never* sings . . .

# but she *hums* all day long!

Songbirds

# Doctor Duck

Story by Julia Donaldson
Pictures by Deborah Allwright
Series editor Clare Kirtley

**OXFORD**
UNIVERSITY PRESS

# Tips for reading Doctor Duck together

This book practises these letter patterns:

ng  ck  x  qu

Ask your child to point to these letter patterns and say the sounds
(e.g. *qu* as in *queen*). Look out for these letter patterns in the story.

Your child might find these words tricky:

he  I  of  said  she  some  to
was  came  come  days  doctor

These words are common, but your child may not have learned how to
sound them out yet. Say the words for your child if they do not know them.

Before you begin, ask your child to read the title by sounding out and
blending as much as possible. Look at the picture together. What do you
think this story is about?

Remind your child to read unfamiliar words by saying the individual sounds
and then blending them together quickly to read the word. When you have
finished reading the story, look through it again and:

- Ask your child, *Why did Mum ask the doctor to come quick?*
- Find some words that contain the letter pattern *qu* (*quick, quack*). Find
  and read some words in the book which end with the sound *k (duck, sick,
  quick, quack, luck, back, milk, yuk)*. Say what letter patterns make the *k*
  sound at the end of these words (*ck, k*). What other letter can make the
  *k* sound (c)?

# Bob Bug was in his cot.

"Get up, Bob," said Dad.

But Bob did not get up.
"I am hot!" he said.

"Bob is sick!" said Mum. "Quick!
I will ring Doctor Duck."

"Mum is a fusspot," said Dad.

# Mum Bug rang Doctor Duck.

"Come quick!" she said. "Bob is sick!"

"Quack, quack!" said Doctor Duck. He got his box of pills.

"I will mix this pill up with some milk," he said.

"Sip this," said Doctor Duck to Bob Bug.

"Yuk," said Bob, but he
had a sip.

"Quack, quack!" said Doctor Duck.

"I will come back in six days."

When Doctor Duck came back,
Bob was hopping and singing.

But Dad Bug was in bed.
"I am hot! I am sick!" he said.

"Bad luck, Dad," said Mum.
"Dad is a fusspot!" said Bob.

# Practise Your Phonics With Julia Donaldson's Songbirds

By the Author of The Gruffalo

## Look out for the other titles in the series ...

Top Cat and Other Stories
978-0-19-279296-9

The Odd Pet and Other Stories
978-0-19-279297-6

The Ox and the Yak and Other Stories
978-0-19-279298-3

Scrap Rocket and Other Stories
978-0-19-279299-0

Where is the Snail? and Other Stories
978-0-19-279300-3

Tadpoles and Other Stories
978-0-19-279301-0

My Cat and Other Stories
978-0-19-279302-7

Leroy and Other Stories
978-0-19-279303-4

Where Were You Bert? and Other Stories
978-0-19-279304-1